WORDS ON WATER

WORDS ON WATER

**An Anthology of Poems
entered for the Young *Observer*
National Children's Poetry Competition,
sponsored by the Water Authorities
Association**

Illustrated by William Geldart

VIKING KESTREL

Viking Kestrel, Penguin Books Ltd, Harmondsworth, Middlesex, England
Viking Penguin Inc., 40 West 23rd Street, New York, New York 10010, U.S.A.
Penguin Books Australia Ltd, Ringwood, Victoria, Australia
Penguin Books Canada Ltd, 2801 John Street, Markham, Ontario, Canada L3R 1B4
Penguin Books (N.Z.) Ltd, 182-190 Wairau Road, Auckland 10, New Zealand

First published 1987
Published simultaneously in Puffin Books

Typeset in 10/12pt Linotron Trump Medieval
Designed by Sonia Alexis

Printed in Great Britain by
Butler & Tanner Ltd, Frome, Somerset

British Library Cataloguing in Publication Data
Words on water: an anthology of poems
   entered for the Young *Observer* National
   Children's Poetry Competition, sponsored
   by the Water Authorities Association.
   1. Children's poetry, English
   I. Water Authorities Association
   II. The Observer
   821'.914'0809282   PR1195.C47
   ISBN 0-670-81745-7

Contents

IT STARTED TO RAIN

ALL THE WATER TURNED INTO CLOUDS
I BLE'R AETH Y LLYN?

Until I saw the sea

the sea

Until I saw the sea

Until I saw the sea
  I did not know
  that wind
  could wrinkle water
so.

I never knew
  that sun
could splinter a whole
sea of blue.

Nor did I know before,
a sea breathes in and

out

upon a shore.

Gary Hancock, 13

The Sea

Winter is here the sea is irritable,
She crashes against the cliffs
Surging through the blow-holes,
Gushing in fountains of froth and foam.
Making mountainous waves which rage into land,
Leaving a foam-wet shore.
Echoing liquid sounds fill the air
She pounces on the shore with wreaths of white,
She is cruel and her cloak is leaden,
She spumes and sprays in her fury.

Spring is here once more,
The sea in gentle mood,
She gurgles and glistens.
The raging winter is over
She waits anticipating the warmth of summer
She gushes into the rockpools with the smooth spring
    swell.

Summer has at last arrived,
The sun warms the air
Seagulls soar through a cloudless sky,
The golden light glistens on a transparent sea,
The sea herself relaxes –
Lapping up on the arid shore,
The refreshing water reflects happy children's faces
She shimmers in a gown of happiness,
Oh, how she adores the summer.

Autumn is about,
A time of high-tides
Which regurgitate myriads of shells,
The sea is preparing to boil in her winter rage.
And soon the year will begin again,
And the sea will relive her many moods once more.

Ellen Fraser, 11

Camels

The sea gets rough
Getting higher and higher
Multiplying like thousands of camels
Marching across a blue desert.

Steven Jackson, 11

The Sea

When I come to the seaside I hear
that crashing sound.
I love that sound you make.
I like making a sand-cake.
Long ago I left you, now I know it
was a mistake.
I love that sound you make.

When I swim I make a din.
I love swimming in you.
Sometimes I want to burst.
You roar when you are angry and
crash along the rocks.
Everyone makes a mistake.
I miss that sound you make.

Heather Whitehead, 8

Disevolving

As a child it was fun
To spring from the towels,
Aiming straight at the sea,
And have it wrestle me,
My quick stride quenched to slow-motion,
Until – at waist-high –
I could make better going
By lifting up horizontal
And flapping my limbs
Fish-wise.

Joseph Johnson, 18

Crest of a Wave

I watch her movements with obsession,
Hoping for a trace of white.
I listen, sinews straining, silent,
For her thunder in the night.
Impatiently I scan her body
Praying for those early signs;
Somewhere in the blue I see
The shadows of some moving lines.
Then, as if to tease and trick me,
She just lies there, smooth and still;
I continue watching, waiting,
Dreaming of her promised thrill.
Just as hope is almost fading,
She begins a gentle sway,
Slowly rising, heaving, falling,
Tempting me to come her way.
So, at last, I run to meet her,
Stumbling, reckless, nearly crazed –
Till I'm with her, on her, in her,
Breathless, laughing and amazed.

Simon Laird, 15

Seafishing

Fishing?
Just an empty pair of boots,
Sunk deep in gloom beside the rain-soaked sand,
And little wavelets tumbling, pathetic power.

On Wings of Song unfurled its dirty sails
And pushed beyond, and caught the rod that bowed
And bent in gentle breeze above the sea.

From nest secure, wedged deep inside a boot,
A reel, gently winding as the waves took hold,
Relaxed their pull on dead and wasted bait.

The minutes passed like hours, the hours like days,
And the hazy gas of drizzle fell on an empty sea,
Ten square feet of glorious open space,
Where nothing moved but the grey, dark waves
And the blanket of silence.

And the night fell fast as rain,
Like a curtain on a play,
But the man returned for the curtain-call
And the rain on the sea applauded,
And the wind whistled in approval,
But the fish did not come.

Paul Hodges, 15

To Shoot An Arrow

To shoot an arrow that self-same way
Take a small boat and a huddle of men
And cutting rocks all spewed with spray
And a howling storm force ten.

Take a hull all jagged-split and maimed
And a rescue bid in a brimstone squall
How many lives so quickly claimed
By Viking, Malin and Rockall.

For Cromarty sings with dead lost sails
And Portland Bill and Hebrides
The coasts tonight are wreathed with gales
Which tear apart exhausted seas.

With crystal tuned, I am at peace
I hear the voice which soft intones
The weather's backing from the east
But with it come so many moans
Of brave young men with hearts
Now ceased.

Carl Röhsler, 16

Tidal Wave

I was sitting on the beach one day
Just soaking up the sun
When panic broke out around me
And people began to run.
For out there in the distance was a sight I'd never seen
A tidal wave was coming so big, so wild, so mean!
I climbed over the wall so quickly not daring to turn and
    stop
With the sound of the wave approaching, my ears began
    to pop.
The next thing I remember was swimming down the
    street
With cars and buses floating by and even a promenade
    seat!
It carried me into the town centre, I was not even daring
    to look
When it crashed down the doors of the library and out
    came some of the books.
It took me into Woolworths up and down the floors
Then pushed me out the back way going through the
    stores.
On through Marks and Spencers I saw the manageress,
    she did faint

And could hear the manager shouting, 'Stand still girls
We are protected, for St Michael is our Saint!'
Out into Asda Superstore it didn't take much time
To turn the hardware section into soft mud and smelly
   slime.
A man stood there in the corner looking shocked and ever
   so pale
Giving out his orders, 'Put that swimwear there on sale!'
It swept along the food stock there were beans and soup
   floating around
When all of a sudden I noticed the water was going down.
We were slowly going backwards along the way we came
Back up the street, I was pleased to see those red roof tiles
   again.
There goes Marks and Spencers, Woolworths, the library
   too
I hope our drainage is working for there be lots of work to
   do.
I spotted the sea wall behind me it was nearly in my reach
It slowly took me over and dumped me back where I
   started just sunbathing on the beach.
It was then when I heard a voice shouting wake up son
   you've been making a heck of a din
But you can't sleep here any longer for the tide's about to
   come in!

Chris Noon, 11

On the Beach

My great-aunt has cut her leg
On the thorns that skirt the sharp descent.
The blood dyes her stockings a shade of red
So dark it seems to hasten nightfall.
With my stick I proudly slay the guilty tendril
My aunt still walks with a limp.

Down below the stream giggles its way to oblivion
In the sky-coloured ocean
Lurking beyond the rocks,
But soon, I know, to creep again towards the shore
And gnaw at crumbling cliffs.

We crunch along the shingle
To stories of the old pier that they say, once stood here.
My aunt finds one of her special shells
So small, that only she can find,
Which she will place in a chest
Given to her when the sea was young
And so much further away.

Dafydd Foster Evans, 18

The Sea

The sea, it is not humourless,
Despite the grey face it assumes,
It likes to tease the fishermen
With slaps and sprays of brine.

And on stormy evenings
The sea, if feeling mischievous,
Will deftly swipe a man off
To five short printed lines

On sheets already itching
To clasp the ocean's bounty,
Battered, salted, sold,
At fifty pence a time.

Joseph Johnson, 18

The Shetland Boat

There's a lonely sea out there,
And nothing on either side
But the mist and rain,
And the occasional pebbledashed gannet
Flying, its heavy young wings
Jerking on nylon strings of rain.
And the ship dips and rises
More than a toy aeroplane
Outside a crowded supermarket.
And, as it dives expertly

The creatures below sink before it
And spit back gulps of foam.
    And the sea gives way before it
Like earth before a damaged plough
    That cuts against the furrow.
The seed:bread for the following nasal fulmars
    And varnished pirate skuas,
Is little and wasted.
    The black, shiny back of a porpoise
Spins like a finned black cog;
    Always rising and turning.
And the mist closes in
    With the cold and the rain,
And the ship ploughs on.

Paul Hodges, 15

Splashing Waves

The wave
covers me
it creeps up on me
rising from its death.
My seconds won't last long.
Its mighty strength is looking for me.
I'm falling in his trap,
my seconds have gone
I'm stretching for life
trying to hold on
if not it's death.
My purple face,
can't live for ever
but nor can a wave.
The rattle of bones
pulls me down
as if I'm in a trance.
My hands turn to air
not gripping a thing
me falling apart
thousands of me
scattered to a cloud of love
where I belong.

Ross Gentle, 10

One day I saw water in the sea.
Then I thought I'd go home
And put water in my tea.
The sea goes on the sand –
The mouth drinks up the sea.

Paul Webster, 4

Washed Up

A yard of fishing net,
torn rope hugging the silt,
an empty oil drum beating
to the sound of waves.
Jellyfish, stodgy cake mix,
rotting in the sun.

A bar of driftwood
scrawls tiny ditches
on the sand;
the brine seeps
into caves in the wood
and flakes off splinters
on to the moist sand.

An oil-sodden seagull
is tarred to pebbles
and is dead as a wall.
Its liquorice body ruffles
in the bite of the wind.

Bulbs of seaweed
scratch against golden sand
and quiver as the tide nears,
spewing out froth as it comes.
The seaweed disappears
under a mass of water once more.

The tide ebbs
and the treasure trove of debris
moves out to the deeps,
again.

Matthew Goddard, 13

The Sea

The place for me,
Is not the sea.

I might sink,
I think.

Another thing,
Jellyfish sting.

Crabs have claws,
Sharks have jaws.

In the sun,
The waves look fun.

But underneath,
The horrible teeth.

Gregory Allin, 15

Seascape

Seagulls flirt
Their oily underbellies
As a child licks at an ice-cream.

The tide flushes
The creases of sand,
Losing salted specks
At each sweep.

Sand scratches
White on my feet
As the graze on my leg
Bleeds with pain.

Then the tide
Scours away
And flakes
The cool, brushed sand.

The sea air
Tickles the inside of my nose,
Like chalk dust,
Dry.

David Lawrence, 13

Rock Pool

Rock pool, rock pool,
See the sand guzzle
The sour sea.
Each drip of water,
Tasteless and dry.
A swirl of sand
Rubs between my toes,
Worms wriggling.

Faint echoes of ships' horns
Blowing
And the rock pools humming.
A small crab,
Its legs long, thin;
Its eyes,
Size of melon pips.
I touch the crab's shell.
Hard but breakable.
A pebble lies crushed,
Smashed against the tide's
Pestle and mortar.
And now
The pebbles are the sands.

Michelle Saunders, 13

Away down the river

Away down the river

Away down the river,
    Pondskaters glide by.
Their spindly legs, clinging to the water,
    Carry them swiftly away where,
Guided by the movement of a stricken fly
    Those deadly mantis close in for the kill.

Away down the river,
    Whirligigs twirling,
Whirring away on business unknown.
    Little bowlers bobbing,
Fast paddling and beetling,
    The river businessmen make inaudible deals.

Way under the river,
    A camouflaged terror,
Homing in on a beetle, so unaware.
    Snap, gulp,
Downed in a mouthful,
    The tiger of the river glides on its way.

Away down the river,
        A hole in the bankside
No sound from within, the tenants not home.
        The kingfisher's eye spots a glimmering scale,
Dark, splash, grab, dash,
        The green and blue divebomber swallows its catch.

Away down the river,
        The laced gossamers glistening in the bright
            morning sun,
The beautiful body, suspended in air.
        The whirring of wings, riding the air currents,
Dive with precision, just skimming the surface,
        The alien beauty alights on a leaf.

The river flows onwards,
        Not heeding their antics,
Flowing gently to the rising sun.
        From a stream to a brook,
To a wide-flowing river,
        A delicate life web stretched from bank to bank.

Matthew Steer, 12

The Cleddau

The Cleddau starts at St Anne's Head,
With its lighthouse, white,
Warning tankers off the rocks
On windy, foggy nights.

Past Angle with its lifeboat
Towards oil refineries
Where tankers large and small
Unload at jetties.

Past the power station
Supplier of electricity
To the dockyard at Pembroke Dock
From where ferries went out to sea.

Under the Cleddau toll bridge
And as it is so high
The views they cannot be missed
From the highway through the sky.

It flows on through the country
To Picton where it divides,
The Eastern and Western go their way
To where the sources hide.

Andrew Woolnough, 14

A Poem on Water

A poem on water?
It has all been done before.
Not another poem on silent raindrops,
Pit-pattering to the floor?
Rain, rain falls on the window pane.
Can you take any more?

The wide and mysterious oceans,
Or the Mediterranean sea,
The graceful blue whale,
Or the simple water-flea,
All get nothing out of ten
For originality.

Julian Lynn, 14

The Pond of Fulfilment

In a place I know
There is a quaint mysterious pond.
Many people have looked into it
And seen many a wished-for thing.
An angler passing by looked into it
And saw himself landing a two-foot tench;
A gardener looked in and saw his garden,
The most beautiful ever;
A sailor looked in and saw
A fine new galleon just for him;
A tramp looked in and saw a delicious meal;
But none of those people took heed of their chances!

Along came a famine-stricken Ethiopian –
He looked in, and saw a refreshing pool of water
And he went in for it, and was rewarded.

John Diller, 11

Yesterday

I see the murky slime that has replaced the clear, eddied
   water.
And I pity my father.
For his were the days when the barges sailed,
flamboyantly and gaily up the waterways.
His were the days when the churning waves lapped at the
   sturdy gates.

But now I see no burnished locks.

The worn path that the horses trod on and traced the canal's serpentine course is brimming with overgrowth.

And I silently cry as I recall his gravelly voice echoing up and down the boons of the canal.

For while I have my future among the clouds his died long ago.

It died with the canal and the sunken barges.

The grey, green of the rampageous waters, stagnant now, littered with refuse was his life.

How he loved the sloshing waters! How he worshipped Ireland's waterways!

And I pity my father because a ceasing of gaily barges has closed the locks to all.

His old water abode has gone, gone for ever to the dregs.

My father tearfully shrugs off his youth but refuses to look at the sordid, silent waters that hide a prestigious past.

For the waters were quenched by the oilfields of Arabia.

And no more do they carry Ireland's trade.

For the waters sigh daily as more insults are heaped into their bodies, for the old canal holds bottles and cans.

The festering, gemmy waters imbower a strange predicament for my father.

And I pity my father embossed upon the waterways for his eyes are welled with tears while I in all my modern glory smile at the plane.

Sinead Dooher, 14

Following the River

The lake lies blue and gleaming
   while the osprey sings above the wind.
The trout in the rivers are swimming
   through the leftovers of friends.
Gushing over rocks of white and grey
   are the waters of the spring,
Bubbling like a geyser of mud and clay.
Flying like a bird are the salmon of the cold,
Jumping over ice waterfalls carved like a horn.

Further down the river are the gloomy brown waters of
   the crocs,
Sleeping with their mouths wide for the scavengers to
   pick the dirt off the teeth shining clean.
Near the sandy beaches swimming like an otter comes an
   alligator looking for his prey.
Yellow blue and green comes a dragonfly,
Hovering for a minute through the clear bright sky.
White fluffy clouds are floating past, fast and high, and
   the dragonfly darts away into a dark clump of trees.

Suddenly a big splash,
   a man is in the water.
A crocodile awakes from his sleep,
   it slithers to the shallows then to the deep.
He swam to the ladder,
   two steps at a time.
Scrambling over the side,
He turns on the bath and puts in the plug,
He boils up the kettle and drinks from his mug.
Pulling the weed out of his hair,
   he gets in the bath in his underwear,
Slowly the bath gets deeper and deeper,
Slowly the water gets warmer and warmer.

The boat starts going back down river,
They had seen the waterfall ahead,
Leaving the crocs and aligs behind.
Slowly the river got wider,
Slowly you could start to see the sea,
Slowly the sea got closer and closer,
Then we were right at the foot of the sea.
I saw a fin in the water,
    I knew it was a hammer head shark,
I got off the boat and went to the harbour.

Christopher Barker, 8

Anger

The Water hides its anger
as it destroys
it grabs the broken branches
underwater
and sucks the sap out of them
it blows it to the surface.
Slowly the river becomes a
death chamber
for all that enters
the pretty surface: but
deep down it's a grave.

Martin Hicks, 10

Stillness

The water is still
Except for a trickle of breeze
Through the curving willows.
A piece of crust,
Left by the flustering ducks,
Drifts gently out
Like a graceful swan.
Mud stirs
And the crust is suddenly immersed
In a battle of swirls and swells.
They stop.
And a fanned-out fin
Breaks the surface.

Then comes a telescopic mouth
And with a suck and a gargle
The crust is gone with the great carp
To the decaying bottom.
An angler whips his fine tackle
Out to the quivering reeds,
While a timid water-vole
Scurries through the overhanging grass
And into the water.
His ripples die
And sink.
The water is still.

Jamie MacDonald, 13

The Seduction
(A Clumsy Poem of
Teenage Angst!!!)

After the party, early Sunday morning,
He led her to the quiet bricks of Birkenhead docks.
Far past the silver stream of traffic through the city,
Far from the blind windows of the tower blocks.

He sat down in the darkness, leather jacket creaking
   madly.
He spat into the river, fumbled in a bag.
He handed her the vodka, and she knocked it back like
   water,
She giggled, drunk and nervous, and he muttered 'little
   slag'.

She had met him at the party, and he'd danced with her
    all night.
He'd told her about football; Sammy Lee and Ian Rush.
She had nodded, quite enchanted, and her eyes were wide
    and bright
As he enthused about the Milk Cup, and the next
    McGuigan fight.

As he brought her more drinks, so she fell in love
With his eyes as blue as iodine,
With the fingers that stroked her neck and her thighs
And the kisses that tasted of nicotine.

Then: 'I'll take you to the river where I spend the
    afternoons,
When I should be at school, or eating me dinner.
Where I go, by meself, with me dad's magazines
And a bag filled with shimmering, sweet paint thinner.'

So she followed him there, all high white shoes,
All wide blue eyes, and bottles of vodka.
And sat in the dark, her head rolling forward
Towards the frightening scum on the water.

And talked about school, in a disjointed way:
About O levels she'd be sitting in June
She chattered on, and stared at the water,
The Mersey, green as a septic wound.

Then, when he swiftly contrived to kiss her
His kiss was scented by Listerine
And she stifled a giggle, reminded of numerous
Stories from teenage magazines…

When she discovered she was three months gone
She sobbed in the cool, locked darkness of her room

And she ripped up all her *My Guy* and her *Jackie*
   photo-comics
Until they were just bright paper, like confetti, strewn
On the carpet. And on that day, she broke the heels
Of her high white shoes (as she flung them at the wall).
And realized, for once, that she was truly truly frightened
But more than that, cheated by the promise of it all.

For where, now, was the summer of her sixteenth year;
Full of glitzy fashion features, and stories of romance?
Where a stranger could lead you to bright new worlds,
And how would you know, if you never took a chance?

Full of glossy horoscopes, and glamour with a stammer;
Full of fresh fruit diets – how did she feel betrayed?
Now, with a softly rounded belly, she was sickened every
    morning
By stupid stupid promises, only tacitly made.

Where were the glossy photographs of summer,
Day trips to Blackpool, jumping all the rides?
And where, now, were the pink smiling faces in the
    picture:
Three girls paddling in the grey and frothy tide?

So she cried that she had missed all the innocence around
    her
And all the parties where you meet the boy next door,
Where you walk hand in hand, in an acne'd wonderland,
With a glass of lager-shandy, on a carpeted floor.

But, then again, better to be smoking scented drugs
Or festering, invisibly, unemployed.
Better to destroy your life in modern, man-made ways
Than to fall into this despicable, feminine void.

Better to starve yourself, like a sick, precocious child
Than to walk through town with a belly huge and ripe.
And better, now, to turn away, move away, fade away,
Than to have the neighbours whisper that 'you always
    looked the type'.

Eileen McAuley, 17

River Blythe

In the summer I waded the Blythe.
Slipping on muddy flints
I travelled the length of the river.
At one point
Baby eels sucked at my toes
And tiny water spiders secretly
Hid between specks of sand.

On and on
The soft mud
Grudgingly let my walking stick
Sink into its oozy layers.

Then – a reed laced with dirt
Where a kingfisher
Dashed nearby into
The murky below
And caught a minnow.

On under the bridge
Where nothing grew,
Except slippery slime.
Flounders scudded
As I kicked duckweed.

I clambered up the sun-baked riverbank.
Pieces of earth
Crumbled like a biscuit
Into the water below.
Satisfied,
I made my way home.

Matthew Watson, 13

An Ant's Sea

An ant's sea is a puddle.
Not always there,
Here today, gone tomorrow,
No sharks or swordfish,
No dangers,
Ants have no boat.
Instead a twig,
Twig crossing,
Leaf ferries,
Bark surfboards with petal sails
And bark row-boats,
Now that's an ant's sea.

Stephen Raggatt, 9

Help Me

I am nothing
I am nothing but a little
a little Fish no harm
no harm I do
Oh no oh
the sticky blackness is here
no more I am

Anthony Fountain, 10

Baby Dragonfly

Jaw snapping creature looking for food.
Living among slime.
Waiting to turn into a creature with wings.
Brown creature looks like it's jumped into a jar of
    Marmite.
Eyes sticking out on end as though it's seen a ghost.
Feelers that move around like worms.
Jaws bounce out as he catches his prey.
Next year he's a beautiful dragonfly.

Kerry Sibbett, 9

The Terrapin

His tortoise-shell back, a barnacle
Clutching at the painted algae.
His pipe cleaner neck rigid,
His lonely head shunts to one side, staring into nothing,
The lamp-lit world empty without his shy companion.
His grim features seem to say,
'Where's my friend? Where's my brother?'
He rolls into the water
And attacks his reflection in the glass.
As the gravel swirls, sandstorms arise –
Now the tank is a smoke sheet, a creeping fog.
Then – out of the mist, a prehistoric fossil clambers to its
    rock
To wait alone for its own end.

Matthew Shepherd, 11

Our Pond

In one corner,
under the paving,
lives a grass snake;
he looks like a creased-up old drinking straw
and swims around
eating the pondskaters,
scraps of tinfoil,
frail and easily broken.

Newts live in that pond;
they are lazy,
sun-worshipping sticks.
Any movement,
and each stick finds legs and dashes to safety.

The water snail,
living in hermit fashion,
and coated with algae,
wants only the peace and quiet to eat his meal.

The goldfish,
a lazy mass of flesh poised between life and death,
is still like a picture.

Our pond is a natural habitat;
Man, an outsider.
Please leave Nature at work.

Russell Wood, 12

Canal

Jumping on the stone slabs,
I balance on one leg.
I wobble,
        stumble,
                then fall.
It is cold.
My head goes under and I cannot see.
The thick surface reflects the sun
And looks like tinted glass.
The wall of the canal is covered
With a tapestry of slime,
Wet leaves woven together with hair.
My shoe comes off
And my foot strokes the bottom.
The mud is warm to my toes
And floats to the surface, like strands of smoke.
Air bubbles, too, rise like transparent balloons,
Only to pop at the surface.
The water floods through my clothes
And weighs me down.
Kicking and spluttering,
I rise to the surface, hold my breath,
And sink back down again.
Then up, like a yo-yo.
I am hauled to land, like a captured fish.
But now I can breathe.
The water is still
But a murky patch pollutes the dank surface
And swirls in endless patterns
To settle on the bottom, in my lost shoe.

Sally Clifton, 11

Misty Morning

A white blanket covering the town,
A gull flies
Gone
It flew through the blanket.
You breathe
A white ghost comes out of your mouth.
You run
All around white.
Let me out!!! you yell
No
But you are still stuck.
Another blanket comes out
It goes on the other one,
It gets worse.

Martin Cox, 9

The Frog and Moses

The bright sun beats my wet back;
Bulrushes sway
As I sit on a lily pad,
An anchor stalk plugged to the bottom.
A black cat stalks in the grass behind.
I prepare to spring;
Great pulleys of muscle rebound and...
Plunge
Straight down!
But look –
A beige raft of wicker.
My back legs expand
And I paddle to the surface,
Peep out to see...
A basket with...
I hear a girl coming;
I linger then dive,
Swim to the bank and watch.
She notices the basket,
Her dress swaying in the water.
The lid is lifted,
The peacefulness is broken.
A baby cries.

Rachel Hammond, 12

The Marsh

The bog,
a plate of sticky treacle,
waiting for the unsuspecting
to slip,
die.

A sign,
danger red,
rises above the mist,
like an oil rig
in the North Sea.

The mixed smell
of cow-dung and polluted water
floats on the breeze,
stinging my nostrils.

I lean on a post.
Green mildew clenches my glove,
while the dew paints my shoes,
then creeps up,
weighting the bottom of my jeans.

The soft lowing of cattle
seems to haunt the marsh.
A robin sings his jingle,
A soft sweet warbling,
rose among thorns.

Scott Dougal, 12

The Garden Drain

Black, rusty iron separates the vertical tunnel.
Bottle green bricks line
The passageway to darkness.

On a sunlit afternoon,
I would lie, imagining,
Crawl over to the drain and wonder.

Insects exploring, dodging
The grated light.
Water, stagnant, as thick as oil.
Dies.

Helplessly twigs dive,
Encounter the bottom –
And then resurface.

Drip, drip, drip –
Descant rhythm.
Echoes.

Slime, older than the trees around me,
Still silently swells.
The rhythm is disturbed;
Speckles of mud
Ripple.

Blindly, the flies hover round my body.
I leave,
But the drain will never die.

Caroline Ward, 13

The Pit up the Lane

Up the lane lies a scum-covered pit,
So dirty that a dipped finger could turn black.
Dangerous.
Patches of the sky lie on the surface,
Like huge lily pads, floating.
I throw a stone into the air.
It seems hours before its landing –
Plop; chocolate water sprays,
Causing ripples to grow.
Closer to the water,
The smell of rotted wood and rubbish rises to me.
One tree, half falling, leans over the surface,
An old man on a walking stick,
Frail, rotted.
Leaves are scattered like sawdust in a workshop;
Branches, twisted and bent, form a maze on the water's
    surface.
At night the stars are captured in an ocean of darkness
And the moon lies asleep on floating wood,
Swaying on a bed of ripples.

Stephen Taylor, 13

53

Glide of a Swan

Layering water laps against a streamlined body.
An elegant neck holds an important position.
A slow gliding movement completes an important look.
Inquisitive eyes
Gazing into dark swirling water.
An unmechanical twitch weaves a pattern amongst dark
    reflections.
Even small ducks wind round the procession.
Jerkily swimming to the rhythm of a jittering song.
A bland empty sky holds a piercing breeze,
As away the graceful procession leads.

Emma Pearson, 11

Life Under Water

Under the water it's like a foggy mystery,
it bubbles like the inside of an Aero.
Then the Aero parts,
then they bubble to the surface
in shapes of clouds.
Then one by one they fizz then pop
and the line of the fishing rod gets tangled.
The hook tears the weed,
the doughy bait slowly goes to the bottom like
Halley's Comet.

Guy Plumb, 8

The River

The clear, slow running river
is a two-way mirror.
Fish stare up at me
through my reflection.

A kingfisher,
a spectrum of colours,
perched on an overhanging tree,
studies the still waters,
its beak a sharpened spearhead.
A silver torpedo
fins past.
A flash of blue spark,
a dart in the bull's-eye.

An orange-peel sunset
lies on the water.
Coke cans and
brown crisp packets
bob up and down like plastic ducks
on the scarlet mirror.
A running stream of warm blood.

As I stand back, knee deep
in the deathly silence,
only the ripples slapping
against my boots,
fear rises in my throat,
a weird feeling.
Through the nettles and brambles
I pull my boots
from the black oozing mud –
and run.

Malcolm Goodwin, 13

Blocked Drain

An old building.
In the damp kitchen
I turned on the tap.
I waited.
No water;
only a few drops
which splattered into the dry stained sink.
I strained my eyes
for the stopcock
in the darkened corners of the room.

I found it, rusted.
I turned it
and water rushed through the pipes,
washing out those loose rusted pieces.
I started to clean the brushes
but soon the water filled the sink.
Somewhere was blocked.
I went outside
and there was the blockage –
the drain, packed with mud.
A sharp prick
and water trickled down my arm.
I thought I had cut myself.
The pipe was clear
and water from the sink came gushing out.
Now the drain.
I shoved my fingers through the slimy wet slush;
I scraped the remaining mud
away with my hand:
leaves, mud, stones, and water
slowly oozed through my fingers.
I turned on the tap.
The water rushed freely
down the drain.

Michial Cook, 13

Bullfrog

In the river I sit;
On a leaf I stay,
Watching the baby
Floating down the river,

Rocking gently on the shivery water
In the steamy sun.

I wonder why he is on the water…
I wonder why he is in the basket…
I wonder why…

But still I sit on the water;
On a leaf I stay,
Still watching the baby drifting
Dreamily away.

Marie Cantwell, 11

Fate

Mud rises like a chiffon scarf
dancing with green slime partners;
a smell of sickness.
A tarred basket made from reeds.
Containing what?

I peer in and see a bundle,
two dark eyes peering into a forest of bulrushes
and a mouth opening and shutting
while the body struggles,
restless in the bands of linen.
The water settles.
But the dying and killing
Never stop.

Caroline English, 12

Dragonfly

In a hovering limbo, both
Beauty and beast.
Skimming wet summer air,
A flutterer of dreams,
Or a grotesque oily insect.

A kind of haunting, or
A kind of loving.
The ponds of stagnant green, reeds
Hidden in the hot, leafy woods of shade
By deepest July.

To live for a day,
Then to sink again
Into the watery blackness of no time. But
It's enough.
It's all we can ask for.

David Mitchell, 17

That Pond!

Swiftly gliding about,
Suddenly tipping up a little,
The water making a V shape after the boat.
We were screaming for joy.
Then, turning around and heading for the shore.
Elizabeth gradually stepped out.
I wanted to go with her,
Like a little child wanting to go with her mother.
I was about to step when…
Elizabeth shouted, 'Hang on!'
Too late…
I fell in.
Haaah!
Help!
Splashing about.
The taste of the slimy dirty water,
The ducks flying out of the way,
Their wings spread,
And shouting that they had been disturbed.
Elizabeth slowly hauled me out.
Standing on the shore dripping wet,
The squelchy feeling of water in my boots,
Like a soggy squelchy jellyfish.
I ran home
And went into my bedroom, crying.
Then – feeling of clothes
And warm air round me.
I felt glad to be at home –
But
That pond!

Rosalind Roberts, 11

It started to rain

Changes

As I walked down Lower Clarence Road,
past the station and lorry park,
it started to rain.
The road was long, dirty and boring.
I looked back at the station dome.
The two small round windows
seemed like surprised shy eyes.
The dull silver dome seemed to wear a hat,
and the straight chimneys against the dome
looked like thick lines of hair.
This animal looked as if
it was a sweet loving creature.
It was getting wet and its hair became darker.

Then gradually I began to feel cold
like a block of soft ice,
all smooth, gentle and solid
but not hard.
My hair felt soggy and slightly sticky,
a bit like trees.
When I pulled wet clumps of hair
further and further apart,
it seemed as if the trunk got shorter,
and the branches longer.
As the rain from my hair fell on to my face,
I felt as if a wet cloth was being put over my head
and that I was slowly changing
from being a dry Thing
to being a wet Thing.

Sometimes the rain just spat slightly.
It also rained big drops,
making me feel black and heavy.

The rain made other things look very beautiful.
Spiders' webs, grass,
any weed flowers especially.
Because raindrops got caught
in the middle and on the petals.
It made the pebbles sparkle
in the broken tarmac, like precious stones.
I looked into a puddle.
I saw a reflection of myself and the
ivy on the fence of the lorry park.
As raindrops fell on the puddle,
it made the puddle shake
and my reflection went all wobbly.

The raindrops fell on the puddle
making circles.
Getting bigger and bigger.
Things change in the rain.
People move faster
and put up their umbrellas.
It gets a bit colder.
Everything sparkles and glistens in the rain.

Hannah Chambers, 8

Window Pane Rain

It's two snails running a race.
It's a dot-to-dot puzzle.
It's someone crying.
It's a winding road or river.
It's somebody throwing overripe tomatoes at a wall
    and then all the juice running down and making
    mysterious patterns.

It's a never-ending maze.
It's a slug's trail on a hot and dusty path. In the middle
     of summer
It's splashes of ink on a piece of blotting paper.
It's a mysterious wood in the middle of nowhere on a dark
     and creepy night.
It's a graveyard at night with the icy fingers of an
     imaginary ghost clinging to you.
It's old men's bony fingers.
It's ivy climbing up the wall of an old ruined castle.
It's me when I'm bored and miserable.

Tara Sheehan, 14

The changing Season

Making umbrellas burst out into full bloom
Forcing the 'wet day' sign up
Hammering hard on a leaf-green mini
Corroding the bodywork to an autumn rust.
The dry drains are filled by the long-awaited
Rain harvest.
Turning the dead, dry grass
To a muddy slosh
Thunder roars with laughter
As it forces the crowds to scurry
Like squirrels inside,
Changing the world
Like the turning from season to season.

Suzanne Begley, 12

The Ark

I am the ant,
The ant who boarded the world
In fright at the first drop of rain
That could kill me.
I am the ant.
My memory reflects in outside worlds
Of sweet mint air.
Now,
The smell of sweat and dung decayed.
My small body hides
Where an elephant stamped impatiently
And where a man crouched under creaking boughs,
Clasped hands together and prayed.
A drop of rain
And my unbelief surrenders.
And then the motion of sadness;
The rank smell of fresh gopher wood fills me.
Yet worse –
My tiny nostrils sense stricken panic
From the outside world.
The stretch of water is endless
And already
Bodies of black and white rhinos,
Bloated with water,
Clot the surface
And a layer of insects smothers,
A covering for the already dead.
I crawl inside
And sit in a crevice
Watching the destruction
While forty days and nights pass on.
Then the dove gives thanks:

The world,
Two of each,
Will live on.

Charlotte Hawthorn, 13

Water

I like the town on rainy nights
When everything is wet
When all the town is sparkling bright
And streets of shining jet

When all the rain about the town
Is like a looking-glass
And all the lights are upside down
Below me as I pass

In all the pools are cloudy skies
All down the dirty streets
But a fairy city gleams and lies
Below me at my feet

Jonathan Watson, 13

Like Hell

She stooped over the wash tub,
   Small and spare,
Wrestling
   With uncontrollable greying garments,
Straightening up
   To stand on tiptoe
And push them into the ageing mangle.
   Spreadeagled against the rollers,
Heaving with effort,
   The surplus water ran
From bony wrists
   Along the blue-white underside of tiny arms
Into savagely hollowed armpits,
   The warmth giving away
To an ever pleasant coolness,
   Continuing over bare ribs,
Down meagre thighs,
   To make drenched rags of skirt
Which clung about her legs.

She turned the handle,
Ever and again
     Mustering all the power of nine short years
And could have been ninety.
     Tears of desperation
Clouded her eyes.
     Between rasping tortured breaths
She begged it would be a fine day,
     But it rained…

Elizabeth Alison, 13

Rain…Rain…

The lights are all on though it's just past midday;
No one can think of a bright word to say.
It rained all yesterday, it's raining today;
A grey world outside, inside me it's grey.

I stare out of the window, fists under my chin;
The gutter leaks drips on the lid of the bin.
When they say 'Cheer up!' I manage a grin,
It's sodden outside, I'm sad within.

Bubbles and bits pour into the drains;
Clouds smother the sad laments from the trains.
The moisture has seeped inside to my brains…
It's raining outside, inside me it rains.

Danielle Rhodes, 15

'Rain Stopped Play'

Many a poem has been written about rain,
Though these are mainly all the same;
(About the way it pitters and patters,
Nothing at all about what really matters).
But this is to do with the game of cricket
And the way the rain affects the wicket.
The yorker skids and the bouncer rolls,
Troubling little, save daisies and moles.
Many a batsman has been stopped in his tracks
As the rain trickles down and fills in the cracks.
And many an innings has been made forcibly
To run to the pavilion for an early tea.
But many a captain, in the midst of despair,
When he's lost cheaply his opening pair,
Has raised his eyes upwards and has said,
'I wish the clouds would form overhead.'

And that afternoon,
On the brink of doom,
When you look towards heaven
And you're twenty for seven,
You breathe sighs of relief,
It's the end of your grief,
As you hear the umpire say,
'Sorry lads, rain stopped play.'

James Davies, 16

The Flood

Water, water all around,
Flooding over flattish ground,
Aunty Nellie's kitchen table
Floating past the baby's cradle,
And Sooty, the big, fat, tabby cat
Afloat in Grandma's Sunday hat.

Mother's best, blue Wedgwood china
Drifting like an ocean liner,
Wogan gurgling in the corner
Then starts steaming like a sauna,
The TV blows up into bits
And Dad says, 'Wogan's had his chips.'

Grandad standing, frying kippers,
In his wetsuit and his flippers,
Billy standing on the stair
Dressed only in his underwear,
'This is fun,' young Billy cried
As through his Granny's legs he dived!

Mother said, 'I've had enough!
I'm sick and tired of this floating stuff.'
But then Aunt Milly looked and frowned

And said, 'I think poor Nellie's drowned.'
'I always knew,' said cousin Kim,
'That Nellie should have learnt to swim.'

Round the corner came the fire brigade
On a life-saving crusade,
But once they saw the chaotic fuss
They said, 'This is no job for us!
We'll have to call the lifeboat crew
To man-the-boats and rescue you!'

Karen Antcliffe and Emma Evans, 10

Sculptured Leaf

Abstract light reflections
Bending slowly round the glossy shell,
Droplets model an exact double,
Gently creating a delicate sculpture
The soft edge gently guiding strands of water
Into a precious globe reflecting the glow of its
    surroundings,
Molten glass rolling down the green surface
Like crystal teardrops.
An army-green leaf holds a cool aura of nature
Reflecting coolness.
Covered in mercury
A clinging metallic liquid
Sucking its magnet-like body along the sculptured leaf.

Emma Pearson, 11

Noah's Ark

The cow's body
like a map.
The giraffe's neck
like a ladder.
The monkey's ears
ready to take off.
And Noah's print
in cow dung
like a big black hole
drying fast.
The spiders in the corner
spinning their
riches of wet pearls.
The elephant wrinkled
like a closed-up hand.
The parrot talking,
performing its act.
The apes' holloas
like foghorns.

While outside
the sea is drowning
and the ark riding its waves.

Emma Smith, 13

Winter Waterfall

Like a master ventriloquist,
Lips frozen shut, in teeth of ice,
But the voice still booming.

Keith Heddle, 16

Tree Collection

Rain water,
Collected in the stump of a three-way tree,
Ripples
Like a transparent blanket
Shaken between two people;
Only no dust is blown up.
Tiny fragments of bark falling,
Like melted icicles,
Gently slide into the water.
The specks rock back and forth, like a cradle,
As they slowly sink down.
As the wind drops,
An autumn leaf floats on the surface,
Its once crispy skin,
Soggy,
Like clothes soaking in the kitchen sink.
A beetle comes crawling down the trunk,
As if stalking a life or death prey.
A metallic spectrum
On its jet-black back
Glitters in the sun.

I listen hard;
The wind is rustling the first leaves of spring,
A mother soothing her baby.
No other sound;
The whole world seems to be silent for me,
Just how it should be,
As I gaze into my miniature universe.

Lara Mair, 10

Waiting for Water

The world is panting.
Stale and salty water lubricates our embrace;
I flop like a dying jellyfish,
                    drying –
You, wet, like a dog gone swimming,
                    shake your head.

In the pearldamp morning we filled the ice-cube trays
Like a prayer for a cool afternoon, but
The drinks and the freezer are in the next room:
Too far to bother…

The Earth is panting, and
Some energetic television event
Is urging our sweatstained consciences
To relieve her thirst.
But the placid agonized eyes,
The bloated black bellies
Wait like our hopeful ice…
Too far to bother.

Esther Wheatley, 18

Water Restrictions

During our recent dry spell
I saw the pictures on the news:
The drought in Africa.
From young children to old men,
All slumped on the ground, dumb;
Senseless of the buzzing flies
On their sun-scorched faces.
And skeleton-babies,
Jigsaws of bone sewn up in skin,
Sucked sleepily at dry, flaccid breasts,
While frightened mothers rocked back and forth.
I listened, concerned, to the news correspondent,
Looking out of place in his shirt-sleeves,
While he, also seeming concerned, made his
Clinical commentary on the newsworthy suffering.

Then I stretched and switched off –
The picture shrank to a dot
And vanished.

I went out and, over a drink,
Complained bitterly to friends
Of the inconvenience of not being able to
Clean the car with the hosepipe.

John Andrew, 18

Island's Thirst

This year instead of a postcard
I am sending you a grain of sand,
So you can hold the smallest part
Of this sunburnt island in your hand:

Part of this blistered shore where we tourists lie –
Sweating meats laid on a grill,
While on the turquoise crinkled-cotton sea
Through a sundazed shimmer the windsurfs spill;

Where mountains like giant spilt sandcastles
Are bitten off and chewed by the sea,
Rasped rough by the wind, blasted dry,
Sunscalded and scoured to sand in the heat.

One sunburnt island, one baked grain of sand
One blistering thirst.

A sunburnt island of oven-ready sand,
Where the dusty path clings to your feet

Parched and prickling with chirping insects,
Frying in Ambre Solaire on the beach.

Frying! Steaming tarmac oozes heat,
Mirages of puddles gleam on the road,
And a car engine, like a sealed can of beans
In the oven, overheats and then explodes.

Soil desiccates to dust on this island,
Crickets jump like popcorn on a tray;
Coarse thistles grow dry parchment leaves
And dogs with dried-seaweed tongues pant in doorways.

One sunburnt island, one baked grain of sand
One throat-blistering thirst.

Look, from the sunbleached crumbling doorways
Over the bay lies a misty veil,
Shrouding in cloud the spilt-sandcastle mountains
While the wind changes, confused, in the sails.

So when I send to you my grain of sand
From the island sun-scorched hot and raw,
I want you to taste the first few drops of rain
To christen this thirsty, sandpapered shore.

Katy Daniel, 16

All the water turned into clouds

I ble'r aeth y llyn?

The Water Poem

A room full of scribbling schoolboys,
hunched like mice, despairing
outside a locked larder of ideas.
The half images formed
of rivers and waves,
snatched at, and lost
in the crossing of a line.
Of rich desert oases
drifting like the ink in the pen.
Of the crashing waves
scratching at the beach
but lost in the sea of sighs.
Some stare blankly,
dazed like floundering fish.
Others write in drips,
or sudden surges of inspiration.
Most just try to fill the page.

Alone the teacher sits, silent

in his own world of dreams,
dreading the nightmare,
the drowning deluge of poems –
the marking that is to come.

Nicholas Shannon, 13

Water

The ice-cap slowly melts and drops,
    Tall icebergs float among tall ships.
From Arctic wastes the waters flow,
    To make the seas and oceans grow.

Tempests and tides and roaring waves,
    Have carved out arches, cliffs and caves,
Water creates and shapes the land,
    From mountain range to grain of sand.

Up through the rivers water reaches,
    Past headlands, deltas, cliffs and beaches,
From the rivers, little streams
    Spread through the land in glints and gleams.

The water-tank, up in the loft,
    A liquid cube, pure, cold and soft,
Waits to rush out from tap to air,
    And link you with the Polar Bear.

Leo Carey, 12

Water

Water from the tap
Like a tube of soft glass
Breaking. It chews round my fingers
Like waves breaking.

Water in the bowl
Smooth and sticking
Bubbles climbing down my arm
Like a leech.
I make a beard of bubbles.

Drinking water –
Clear and runs down the back of my throat
Slippery and slidey.
Undrys my mouth.

Water in the bath
If mum doesn't scrub me
It's warm and soothing.
I like water.

Edward Hawkesworth, 7

Load the gun
take aim.
Pull the trigger
and fire.

What no bang?
No bullets?
No. Just a splat
and a splash,
squirt in the eye,
drip from the nose.
Now who's next for a soaking?
My water pistol's great!

Iain Kelly, 5

The Dangers of Water

Water is a dangerous thing to tangle with.
If you don't have enough you die of thirst.
If you have too much you can drown.
Ducks, live on water, and look what happens to them.
Their ducklings get eaten by water rats.

Water is a dangerous thing to tangle with.
Snow, if you melt it, is water.
Snow in the face is not nice.
Convicts in prison get fed bread and water.
What a dangerous thing it can be.

Which is why when I was told to write this,
I thought, 'They won't catch me.'
But then when I saw the prize money,
I decided it was worth the risk.

Katy Dadswell, 10

Sug sug buggly dug

Sug sug buggly dug
Goes the water in the plug.

Anna Chan, 5

Hannah in the Bath

The tap is on.
Droplets of water
Dart out and shatter like sandbombs
On the shiny bath.
The water rises.
A squirt of foam distorts my reflection,
Like a painting being smudged.
Hannah is laid in.
The sudden heat makes her screw up her face,
Like a pug's.
She kicks her legs
And holds her breath with shock.
The foam bubbles up;
Her head is covered.
She beams from ear to ear,
Her mouth like a crescent moon.
Mum takes her out,
Leaving the water to go down the plug.
But where to?

Matthew Booley, 11

Saliva

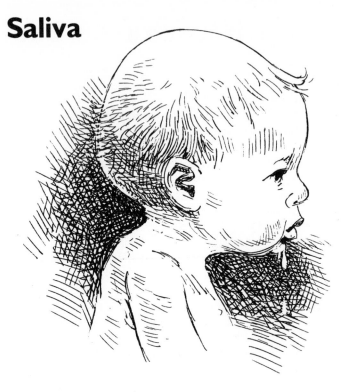

The saliva gathered on the baby's lips
Like foam from an aerosol can.
As it left the baby's lips
It was a new-born bird, struggling to establish itself
And spread its wings.

Then it was lava dripping down a volcano,
Slimy and sludgy, with layers of scum on it.

It progressed into an egg in the frying pan –
Bubbling and spitting as it went.

The saliva gradually became a round, lazy,
Bubbly comet, with an enormous tail in its wake.

As it hung off the chin
It was a drip of treacle about to fall
From an overturned jar on top of the cupboard.

As it let go of the chin
It was a parascender freefalling to the ground.

Adam Clarke, 13

Water

In the creation of the universe, a being was formed.
Let us call him Discoverer; the name is apt.
His was life without death or ageing,
So he wandered the stars, learning as he went
How to build a house, how to shape stone,
A thousand different things: yet there was more.

He was strolling one day under a minty-blue moon,
Watching a shoal of meteorites swoop
When he noticed, gleaming uncertainly ahead,
A patch of dark clarity in a meadow of star-dust.
So he broke off a piece of the crisp fresh moon
And set off, chewing it as he went.

The patch was a pool of transparent liquid –
Discoverer stirred it – splashed it with his hand,
Wondering at the drops that flung through the air
In shattered likenesses of rainbows:
Each reflecting the whole, complete in itself.
He wanted the liquid – but it slipped through his fingers
Like a beautiful dream caught under the sun.

Then: 'Of course!' he cried, and he filled his pockets
Brimful with the dimpling reflections of space.

He hadn't enough – so he moulded stars
To make a bucket, a daisy-chained handle
Dipped and swayed in his massive fist.
His pockets splashed on to roosting rooks
Who grew feathers of stone and flew damply away.
Discoverer laughed. 'What a substance!' he said,
Then paused – 'What a substance – Wata substance –
Water!' He smiled, flicking drops at the moon.
The piece he had eaten had grown back already.
He broke off some more on the way to his home.

Discoverer wanted the frail crystalline beauty
Of water in every room in his house.
He remembered the ponderous rocks,
The grace that water had given them.
Why should not every ugly thing benefit?

He found a piece of potassium-salted cellulose
And sprinkled bright moving drops over its flabby form.
The substance stiffened in surprise – and remained stiff
Even when Discoverer's teeth shredded its life to pulped
    fibre.
'Celery,' said Discoverer – and he moved on.

A jar of yellow powder caught his attention.
It was labelled 'Calc. Carbonate, albumen and vitamins'.
Discoverer remembered the foul stuff well –
A teaspoonful in between meals for indigestion.
He poured some on to his hand, added the water
And gasped as a smooth brown object appeared there.
He was so surprised he dropped it on the carpet
Where a sullen white and yellow stain formed.
Discoverer sighed, picked up the pieces,
Then smiled as he remembered his cupful of magic.
He made another egg, broke it into a bowl
And thoughtfully crunched the shell,
Its yellow eye gazing balefully up at him from the table.

A tiny piece of brown inanimacy lay upon the carpet,
A leftover from the canary's dinner.
Discoverer took it up and carefully fed it a drop of liquid –
Then flung away the writhing mass and hid behind the
    curtain.
When he looked out, a giant threshed the ceiling with a
    hundred arms.
'A…tree!' Discoverer said, 'but too big for this house.'
So he took away the water and picked up the seed where
    it fell on the carpet,
And threw both outside where they grew again –
Twisting and curling in the ecstasy of life.
'Tree-mendous!' said Discoverer. He laughed,
A roaring, vibrating, deeper-than-bass laugh
That shook and cracked the rainbow-shot glassy stars for
    miles.

Discoverer had a problem with plates.
Of course, he used one at each meal
And they accordingly festooned themselves with
    nutritional banners,
Displaying to all and sundry the food he had eaten.
They didn't make his next repast taste too pleasant
    either,
So Discoverer made a new plate for every single meal.
The dirty plates were thrown out to splinter
White grinning teeth against the frigid moon,
Or used to experiment on inside the house
As spades for sand or birdseed or coal-dust.
Discoverer took an old plate he had tried to light the fire
    with
(He couldn't make a new one – too much hard work).
He poured a little water on to it: but nothing happened
Until he tipped it – then he saw the dust and dirt
Running off in desperate streams, choked in cleanliness.
Discoverer was overjoyed – water would make new plates
    for him!

Discoverer's workroom was an anti-gravity area.
This meant that if he dropped a plate it couldn't break
But floated insensible, waiting for him to save it.
Anti-gravity didn't affect Discoverer, though,
So he walked straight in with his starlit pail of water
And tipped it in a glowing stream into the metal sink.
The water didn't appear to like the atmosphere:
It crawled up, over the window, seeking a way out.
Discoverer thought; then reached across and flicked a
    switch.
Three plates he had carefully put on the ceiling
Fell off and broke in front of him – CRASH!
Discoverer didn't really mind. He carefully picked his
    way
Between the bony-fanged pieces to the sink.
The water was happy: it reached out eagerly

For the first dirty plate and suckingly scoured it of food
    and dust.
Discoverer smiled. What were three plates more or less
    when he had water?

Some months later, he noticed a planet,
Third in a series of nine, he thought, or was it?
He dimly remembered a yellow star –
But it didn't really matter where it was
Except that it was just right for that day's dirty dishwater.

Katharine Scarfe Beckett, 13

Tears

MY tears are big and round.
They run down my cheeks.
Just like miniature footballs running down a pitch,
And shooting into an open goal.
Which is endless.
Nobody's tears are just like mine.

Amit Kochhar, 9

The Swallows' Creation

Everything was under water.
The trees were wilting,
The flowers had sunk down into
The mud.
There was no grass.
There were no more people.

A hundred years ago there was a flood and the world was
  drowned.
The water rippled in the stars.
Suddenly hundreds of swallows flew
From the east and they were carrying
An enormous sieve made out of china.
They picked up earth and all the water
Drained out and turned into clouds.

The rowan tree is growing,
The leaves are light green.
Red berries. Red berries.
The green grass is like lots of curved
Eyelashes.
It is a very light night but all
The swallows beating wings down
To the rowan trees make it dark.
When they land they are collecting twigs.
The wings go shhhhoooo.
Some of the swallows are dipping
Into mud puddles.
Everyone is helping to make nests.
One swallow lays three eggs.

One egg cracks then opens
A chick!
One egg cracks and then opens
A girl!
One egg cracks and then opens
A boy!
Slowly the boy and girl climb down
From the nest.
The swallow tells them how
The earth became dry.

That winter the swallow that was
A chick when they were born flies off.
As it leaves them for ever it does
A wing dance.
Shhhhoooo shhhhoooo.

Tansy Hutchinson, 8

Dŵr

fe drenga'r dydd ar y gorwel
    yn fachlud oer.
nid oes yma ond
    dagrau hallt y môr dibaid
    yn dyrnu ar greigiau du.
yma bu hud yn rhyferthwy'r môr,
    bu'r llanw'n llon
    i lygaid plentyn.
gwelwn lwybr aur Na N'og
gwelwn lwybr gwyn y sêr;
    Rhamant a Lledrith
    Tywysogion yr Haf
a deyrnasai'n dirion dros y tonnau glas.
  heriwn yrfeirch gwyn y llanw llwyd
  a chyweirio waliau a chestyll i'w dal:
  fe'u dymchwelwyd ag un llam
  a pharhau'n ddihitio wnâi'r lli.
eisteddwn
  a gwylio dyfod y llanw –
  y llongau'n codi'n ddiog
    arogl gwymon
    cri'r wylan
  a churo tonnau chwil
    ar y creigau du.

ond ffoi a wnawn hyd feysydd
cwsg breuddwydion bore oes.
chwalwyd y rhith
  â tharan carn a gewyn –
    hunllef heddiw
  heb na'fory na ddoe.
llygredd
  yn troelli yn hagrwch gwlyb
  yr enfys sidan;

llygredd
   lle bu glendid y dyfroedd mwyn.
ac nid oes nac aur na gweddi
all buro budredd disglair ddŵr –
   disglair belydrau angau'n gwysio
     tuag adref

         tawelwch isfyd
       a'r glaw yn cropian
      dros ffenestri,
       yn llosgi
   drwy waliau
    cartrefi
     ac eglwysi,
glaw du
   du dros ffiniau gwledydd
   du dros foroedd ac afonydd...

Tcherno...
    cysgodion
   yn llusgo'u
     llwch
   drwy'r lludw
yn garpion o groen ar grwydr:
    ...shima
  a'r glaw
  yn amdo
   tywyll
dros gorff y ddinas dawel.

a thrwy fflamau'r ffwrnais
   daeth
   angau
i dywys y dydd i'w dranc.

ar lannau'r aber draw
   mae cwch

yn disgwyl yn dawel
i dderbyn ei lwch.
galar cenhedlaeth gyfan
yng ngriddfan tost y rhwyfau
ac yn y dagrau brau
yn boddi yn y lli:
aur betalau
yn eurdorch olaf daith
i enau gwawr y machlud oer.

minnau mewn bedd a gleddir
lle nad oes atgof
hiraeth
am fyd ar draeth diderfyn
a dagrau calon
yn dyrnu'r creigiau du:
lle nad oes atgof
am dragywydd daith
y dyfroedd
at ddiddymdra maith y môr.

Nia Roberts, 17

Overheard in a Chelsea Winebar

L'eau.
Neh, feeling quite okah.
Neh!! L'eau, thets whort the Frinch
cawl eet.
Oh wight! But I thowt theh cawled eet
'Perrier'.
Ya, I suppose thets ah translation.
Well, then thars 'Evian'
Neh bubbles, wight?
Ya, comes from glaceyas in the Ealps.
Oh apsolootleah, twes healthea for
wuns physique.

You nea in Stepneh thar Perrier's reallea
dirtea. Its braen!
Braen?!!
Ya, theh cawl eet 'piggiesear'. And
instead of gween bottles, it comes in
braen too!

Good Gawd!
Oh, eets steel gawt the bubbles theau
Neh, neh, neh, misinformed pearson, that
beer. We cawl eet 'Stella Artois'!
Well, whort do theh cawl eet in Stepneh
then?
Ah, I believe eets cawled 'anglah's
orfspwing'...neh...'feesherman's dawtah'
...and eet cums aiht of taips.
Wreally haih interesting we give that
to the hainds!

Sarah Carr, 15

Dŵr

'Dyna fo, mi fyddi'n iawn bellach
        – â gofal yr Arglwydd amdanat.'
Un...Dau ddiferyn,
        dyna'i gyd.
Ond yn fôr o gariad drwy lygaid ei fam.
A dyna fe ar ddydd ei fedydd, yn beichio crio.

        Llifodd y blynyddoedd heibio
ac yn wir, fe gadwodd y diferion sanctaidd eu sêl.
'Roedd yn fachgen hapus,
        â'r bywyd yn byrlymu ohono.

Ond gafael y gaeaf ddaeth â'i bysedd oer
        i newid popeth.
Digwyddiad anochel mae'n debyg.

I ble'r aeth y llyn?
Maes chwarae ydoedd heddiw,
Talpyn gloyw yn llwyfan
        iddo ddangos ei ddoniau.

Un hollt sydyn,
            ac er gwaetha'r ymdrech druenus,
Fe lyncwyd y bwndel –
                glwp.

Glawiodd ar ddydd yr angladd.

Ceril Rhys, 16

Ships

I sit and I dream of that marvellous day when
My ship will come in.
I dream of the comfort that I'll live in then,
And I make plans, and ponder, and change them again;
But I always remember that when the day dawns,
I won't need to worry and make any plans
For the future:
I'll act on a whim.

And as for the bills and the hire-purchase payments,
I'll laugh at them all.
I'll be rid for all time of the monthly encumbrance
Of enticing ads that say 'Pay in Instalments'.
And the times when, now, I'd go into hysterics
Over profits and losses and debits and credits:
They'll be long gone –
I won't miss them at all.

But that's in the future, and, just for the moment,
I sit here and dream.
There's a job to be gone to, but all that can wait,
(Harry will clock on for me if I'm late).
I pretend that I don't know that I'm at the helm
And it's up to me whether I swim or I drown;
I pretend that it's Fate lifts me up, drags me down;
And I sit here and dream
While I drift with the stream.

John Andrew, 18

The Flood

My Dad's temper
Flows with no control,
Neither riverbanks
Nor my mother
Have the power to
Keep the flood between
Boundaries of safety.

Hot blood running
Through arteries.
A central network
Of feeding and
Transporting canals,
Furthering the rage
Until eventual calm.

The waters are
Again placid, once
The sun shines through.

White lip after lip
Laps on to the banks,
Now shattered and torn,
Yet clouds begin to gather...

Helen Agutter, 15

On a use of water

'Left-wing porridge' my friends call it,
And true, it doesn't look too great –
Made with water boiled in kettle,
Dolloped grey upon my plate.
Not for it the creamy whiteness
Of warm milk with yellowed skin,
Nor for it the sticky sweetness
From the Golden Syrup tin.
But for it the grey of water
In a limey kettle boiled,
Charged electric, seething, steaming,
Writhing liquid somehow soiled.
Poured upon expectant oats
Now it mingles, gurgles, clouds –

Water is no longer water.
When stifled by a fibrous shroud,
Nor when flavoured by a capsule
Claiming to be 'sodium-free',
Nor when sweetened by a liquid
Which is 'low in calories'.
But what disturbs me even more –
They say it's all been drunk before.

Fiona Rawes, 16

Body Water

I find it peculiar to think
Water is in your body,
I mean it would be strange
If you had fishes in you.

Imagine fishes in your brain
Or water snails in your bladder,
Maybe an eel or two in your kidney
Or goldfish in your liver.

You could have a tap
In your leg or head,
So I wonder how it's done.
Imagine your seaweed growing under your cap.

I drink lots of water
So, maybe it is that,
That when I drink water it stays in
And let that be that!

Kate Hannay, 8

Drowning

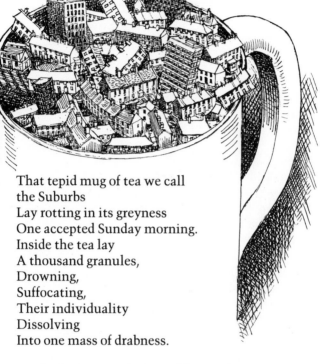

That tepid mug of tea we call
the Suburbs
Lay rotting in its greyness
One accepted Sunday morning.
Inside the tea lay
A thousand granules,
Drowning,
Suffocating,
Their individuality
Dissolving
Into one mass of drabness.

Inside the grey, underheated hospital,
A child was born –
A pink
Happiness
Intruding on the monochrome.
Born to be
Drowned.

Daniel Glass, 14

People Flood

On the old pine table, cracked and worn,
Rests the ghostly white skull of a one time inhabitant;
The predators with jetted feathers have long since gone,
Leaving only a tear of honey.

Remains are few.
Not one admits responsibility.
The green topped guardians have left, ashamed;
The tumbleweeds perform their routine to an unfaithful
    audience.

Civilization deserted the waterpumps when they ran red
And the clouds cried no more.
So the earth was left like a lonely child,
Its throat parched and sore.

A drop of sweat squeezed from the very core;
A single tear from the desperate state
Glistens from the pore, tempted to vaporize,
And in the distance rises up a great fire.

It becomes clearer,
Each flame more distinct.
Hands, so greedy and selfish,
Thoughts of only me...

Overrunning, overtaking, capturing...it is the people
    flood!

Elizabeth Hannam, 16

Woman Drowning, with Child

When the mule was dead
the mother pulled her child away,
Dusted off the dirt and smelling blood,
Took him, left the capes.
His hand
pulled her breast,
Thick milk choked on his face,
Ran into his eyes and nose,
Got eaten by the black flies.
She groaned without seeing
or feeling her tears through the burns,
The boy's gelled eye, or the blooded rocks…

Walking,
Just a long mad fall through the white clouds.

Lord, if she is wanting of anything
it cannot be water.
She has water for blood,
Water to burn.
Cricket as oceans,
Law to drown,
Good labour in drenchings,
England to burst –

Rain never stopped
in discipline, distant trade,
annexation, fiscal relations,
Thick tides of honour,
Cool streams of golden gratitude.

A wash of gas,
and a rocket's smear
of fire on a blistered sky.

She wants nothing
that has ever come,
She has lived thirst
but never loved rainbows,
She's crying now –
like us, we fear.

This water is never safe to drink.

James Dixon, 18

Tap Dripping

The tap is switched off; and all is quiet.
The gushing and rushing and dribbling stops suddenly,
With no warning,
And the man turns his back on the tap.
And yet,
All is not dead, and unable to resist the tempation
He looks once more.
Inside the tubular metal womb, a watery foetus is
    forming and growing.
A transparent dot-baby,
Searching for a way out of its silvery prison.
Bulging and bulbous it trembles,
As it climbs the shiny tunnel looking for an opening.
A throbbing droplet, held together somehow,
A swelling glassy bead.
And suddenly, all at once, it reaches the outlet it has been
    looking for.

It pauses, preparing itself,
And as the man watches – it starts to emerge,
A minute liquid pinpoint at first,
And then the rest.
The tiny ocean is being born.
And just as quickly as it was conceived,
The little dot-baby is about to die.
It trembles one last time,
And with a final supreme effort it frees itself,
And drops into a cup below,
Where it mingles with some old tea, and is lost for ever.
All is quiet.
And the man turns his back on the tap.
And yet,
All is not dead, and unable to resist the temptation
He looks once more.
Inside the tubular metal womb, a watery foetus is
    forming and growing.

Anna Jenkins, 16

At the Baths

I jump off the board, like a bird in the sky.

With a twist and a turn I plough in.
The water is a carpet of moss.
It pushes me back as if it didn't want me.
I touch the bottom, and shoot back up like a flower.
People are screaming.
I take a deep breath and go back,
like a flower dying.

Karl Neary, 11

Lists of prize-winners

Age Group: 10 years and under
1st prize	**The Swallows' Creation**	Tansy Hutchinson
2nd prize	**Changes**	Hannah Chambers
3rd prize	**Cat Sinking**	Jim Balding
Highly Commended	**The Dangers of Water**	Katy Dadswell
	Body Water	Kate Hannay
	Following the River	Christopher Barker
	Anger	Martin Hicks

Age Group: 11–14 years
1st prize	**Noah's Ark**	Emma Smith
2nd prize	**Yesterday**	Sinead Dooher
3rd prize	**Water**	Leo Carey
Highly Commended	**Water**	Katharine Scarfe Beckett
	The Pond of Fulfilment	John Diller
	The Terrapin	Matthew Shepherd

Welsh Prize
	Dŵr	Ceril Rhys
Runner-up	**Dŵr**	Nia Roberts

Age Group: 15–18 years
1st prize	**The Seduction**	Eileen McAuley
2nd prize	**Woman Drowning, with Child**	James Dixon
3rd prize	**The Shetland Boat**	Paul Hodges
Highly Commended	**Island's Thirst**	Katy Daniel
	Tap Dripping	Anna Jenkins
	The Sea	Joseph Johnson

School Prizes
Eynesbury C E (c) School
Huntingdon

Teachers: Richard Reid, Nanda Wisson, Elaine Davies, Ann Rudd

Poems submitted by the school included:

Splashing Waves	Ross Gentle
Anger	Martin Hicks
An Ant's Sea	Stephen Raggatt
Life Under Water	Guy Plumb
Sculptured Leaf	Emma Pearson
Glide of a Swan	Emma Pearson
Misty Morning	Martin Cox
Baby Dragonfly	Kerry Sibbett

Halesworth Middle School
Suffolk

Teacher: Jill Pirrie

Poems submitted by the school included:

Noah's Ark	Emma Smith
Hannah in the Bath	Matthew Booley
The Terrapin	Matthew Shepherd
Fate	Caroline English
Tree Collection	Lara Mair
The Ark	Charlotte Hawthorn
Seascape	David Lawrence
That Pond!	Rosalind Roberts
Bullfrog	Marie Cantwell
Rock Pool	Michelle Saunders
The River	Malcolm Goodwin
Our Pond	Russell Wood
Blocked Drain	Michial Cook
Canal	Sally Clifton
Stillness	Jamie MacDonald
The Marsh	Scott Dougal
Washed Up	Matthew Goddard
The Garden Drain	Caroline Ward
The Pit up the Lane	Stephen Taylor
The Frog and Moses	Rachel Hammond
River Blythe	Matthew Watson

Certificates of Merit

Age Group: 10 years and under

Karen Antcliffe and Emma Evans, Richard Brooks, Tracey Carr, Anna Chan, Kalunga Chisaka, Stuart Clarke, David Coleman, Elizabeth Farthing, Anthony Fountain, Ross Gentle, Edward Hawkesworth, Mark Hawkins, Dorian Holman, Jack Hulme, Iain Kelly, Joshua Kemp, Amit Kochhar, Jenny Lloyd, Tabitha Potts, Jeanette Southern, James Viggers, Emily Wall, Paul Webster, Hester Whitehead, Edward Williams.

Age Group: 11–14 years

Sarah Adams, Shaistah Akhtar, Elizabeth Alison, Louise Bagshawe, Suzanne Begley, Rebecca Brueton, Adam Clarke, Paul Clarke, Josephine Dyer, Ellen Fraser, Daniel Glass, Dominic Goy, Gary Hancock, John Hartley, Steven Jackson, Julian Lynn, Michele Macrerie, Amber Meyer, Karl Neary, Chris Noon, Emma Pearson, Nicholas Shannon, Tara Sheehan, Matthew Steer, Jonathan Watson, Andrew Woolnough.

Age Group: 15–18 years

Helen Agutter, Gregory Allin, John Andrew, Jeremy Bates, Richard Butterworth, Sarah Carr, Andrew Crowther, James Davies, Dafydd Foster Evans, Elizabeth Hannam, Cathy Hazell, Keith Heddle, Paul Hodges, Joseph Johnson, Simon Laird, Robert Leedham, David Mitchell, Fiona Rawes, Danielle Rhodes, Carl Röhsler, Tom Scammell, Robert Tait, Rhiannon Wakeman, Ian Walker, Esther Wheatley.